This Walker book
belongs to:

_____

For Mum

First published 2009 by Walker Books Ltd
87 Vauxhall Walk, London SE11 5HJ

This edition published 2010

2 4 6 8 10 9 7 5 3 1

© 2009 Polly Dunbar

The right of Polly Dunbar to be identified as author/illustrator
of this work has been asserted by her in accordance with
the Copyright, Designs and Patents Act 1988

This book has been typeset in Gill Sans MT Schoolbook

Printed in China

British Library Cataloguing in Publication Data:
a catalogue record for this book is available
from the British Library

ISBN 978-1-4063-2614-7

www.walker.co.uk

Tilly and
her friends
all live
together in
a little yellow
house...

Pretty
Pru

Polly Dunbar

WALKER BOOKS
AND SUBSIDIARIES
LONDON • BOSTON • SYDNEY • AUCKLAND

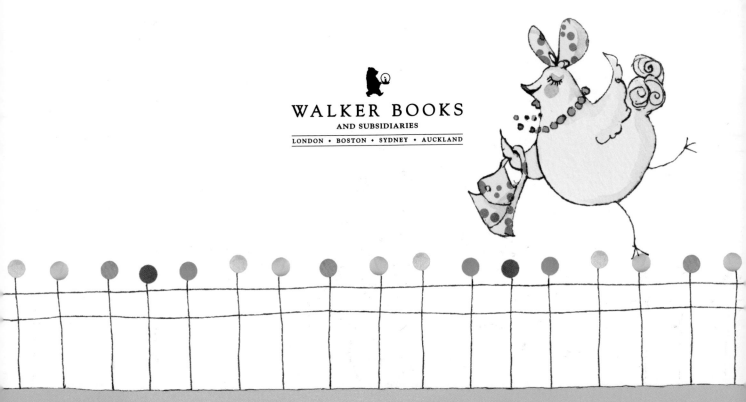

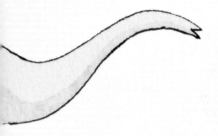

"Oh pretty,"
said Pru,
"I'm so pretty!"

She was

putting on her

favourite

red lipstick.

"Can I have some make-up?" said Tumpty.

"Then I can be pretty like you."

"No,"
said Pru.
"You'll
waste it."

"Humpf," said Tumpty.

So while Pru
was busy doing
a pretty-
prance ...

Tumpty stretched out his very
long trunk and took Pru's handbag!

"Look, everybody," said Tumpty.

"Now we can be pretty like Pru."

"Tilly, Tilly, Tilly,"
Pru called.
"My handbag,
it's lost."

"Don't worry," said Tilly.

"It can't be far away."

"Hello, Hector,"
said Tilly.
"Pru's lost
her handbag.
Do you
have it?"

"No," said Hector.

"My handbag!"
cried Pru,
"my green
handbag
with red
spots.

Tiptoe,
have you seen it?"

Tiptoe blushed

the prettiest shade of pink.

"Doodle!"
flapped Pru.
"Have you
seen my
handbag ...

with my blusher
and nail varnish?"

"It wasn't me!" said Doodle,
and she pointed a very pretty finger.

Everybody laughed ...

everybody except Pru.

"That's
my handbag
on your head,"
said Pru.

Everybody

stopped laughing.

"I'm sorry,"

Tumpty said.

With a curl of his very long trunk,
he gave Pru her handbag back.

"We're sorry too," said Hector.

And they put the make-up back in the bag.

He let
everybody
have a go ...

and they all pranced prettily,

just like Pru.

The End

Polly Dunbar

Polly Dunbar is one of today's most exciting young author-illustrators, her warm and witty books captivating children the world over.

Polly based the Tilly and Friends stories on her own experience of sharing a house with friends. Tilly, Hector, Tumpty, Doodle, Tiptoe and Pru are all very different and they don't always get on. But in the little yellow house, full of love and laughter, no one can be sad or cross for long!

Hello **Tilly**
Polly Dunbar

ISBN 978-1-4063-2550-8

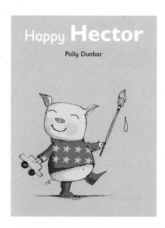

Happy **Hector**
Polly Dunbar

ISBN 978-1-4063-2551-5

Pretty **Pru**
Polly Dunbar

ISBN 978-1-4063-2614-7

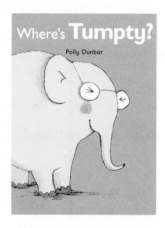

Where's **Tumpty?**
Polly Dunbar

ISBN 978-1-4063-2613-0

Doodle Bites
Polly Dunbar

ISBN 978-1-4063-2615-4

Goodnight **Tiptoe**
Polly Dunbar

ISBN 978-1-4063-2616-1

"Nobody can draw anything more instantly loveable than one of Dunbar's characters."
Independent on Sunday

Available from all good bookstores

www.walker.co.uk